# WHERE'S GUNNERSAURUS?

## THE OFFICIAL SEARCH AND FIND BOOK

™©(2020) THE ARSENAL FOOTBALL CLUB PLC.
ALL RIGHTS RESERVED

ILLUSTRATED UNDER LICENSE BY HENSHAW & DOYLE LTD.
PUBLISHED BY ARENA SPORT.

9781909715998

WWW.ARENASPORTBOOKS.CO.UK

# CONTENTS

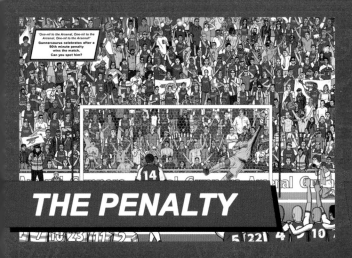

## THE PENALTY

## BIG SCREEN

## HIGHBURY PARK

## CUP FINAL

## VICTORY PARADE

# GUNNERSAURUS

You will find Gunnersaurus hidden on every page, as well as the 'Clock End' clock, the Arsenal Cannons, the Invincibles trophy and a golden boot.

Don't forget to check the back pages for more hidden items!

# HIDDEN ITEMS ON EVERY PAGE

**1 'CLOCK END' CLOCK**

**2 ARSENAL CANNONS**

**1 INVINCIBLES TROPHY**

**1 GOLDEN BOOT**

CHECK THE BACK PAGES FOR 200+ ADDITIONAL ITEMS

Arsenal have invited the fans to watch their final pre-season training session.

Can you see where Gunnersaurus is hiding?

Gunnersaurus has stumbled across a friendly match in his local park.

He is hiding in the crowd...
can you see him?

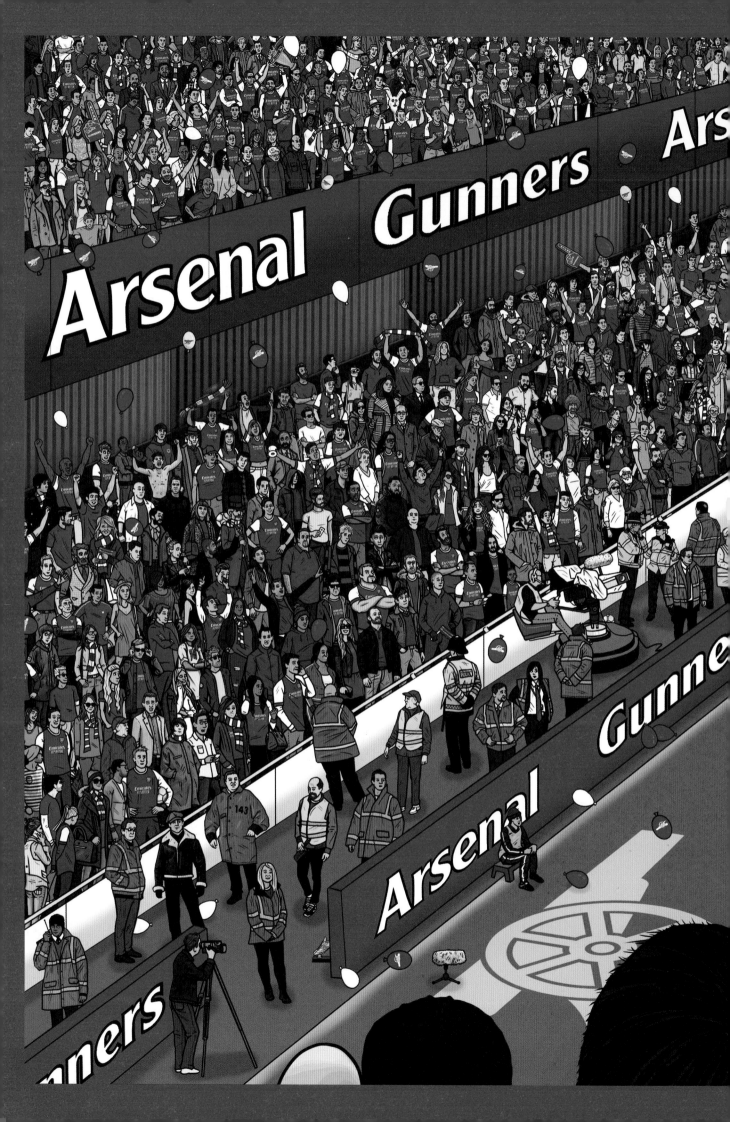

Arsenal start the season in style with an early goal at Emirates Stadium.

Gunnersaurus celebrates with the fans... have you spotted him yet?

Arsenal fans gather at the train station for their first away trip of the season.

Gunnersaurus is trying not to get noticed... have you found him?

It's Cup Final day and the fans have gathered in the parks around the stadium.

Where's Gunnersaurus?

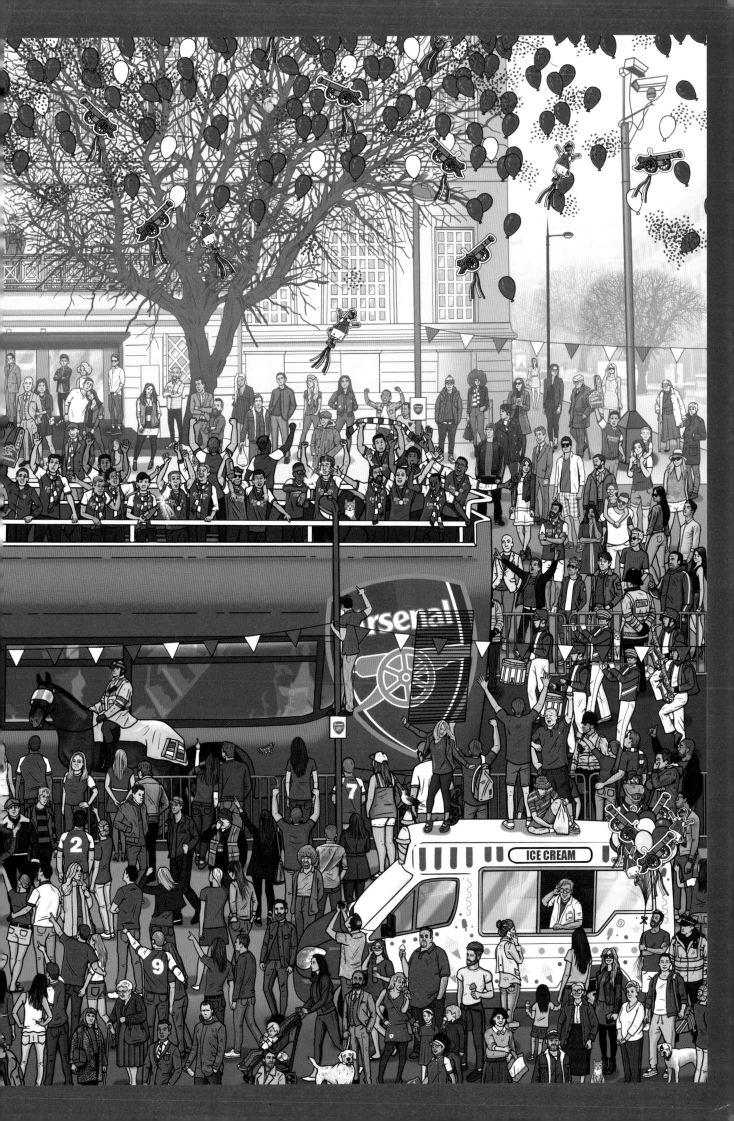

# EXTRA ITEMS

## THE BEACH

- 5 GOLDEN BALLS ☐
- 3 BEACH BALLS ☐
- 3 TROPHIES ☐
- 3 ICE CREAMS ☐
- 3 BUTTERFLIES ☐
- 3 PARROTS ☐

## TRAINING GROUND

- 5 GOLDEN BALLS ☐
- 1 PAIR OF BOOTS ☐
- 3 BLUE CONES ☐
- 3 ORANGE BALLS ☐
- 3 SEASON TICKETS ☐

## LOCAL PARK GAME

- 5 GOLDEN BALLS ☐
- 5 MILK BOTTLES ☐
- 3 SLICES OF PIZZA ☐
- 3 DACHSHUNDS ☐
- 3 SEASON TICKETS ☐

## FIRST GAME OF THE SEASON

- 5 GOLDEN BALLS ☐
- 3 TOILET ROLLS ☐
- 3 CLACKERS ☐
- 3 FOAM FINGERS ☐
- 3 SEASON TICKETS ☐

## TRAIN STATION

- 5 GOLDEN BALLS ☐
- 3 BULLDOGS ☐
- 3 BAGS OF BALLS ☐
- 3 GUNNERS SUITCASES ☐
- 3 SEASON TICKETS ☐

## AWAY GAME

- 5 GOLDEN BALLS ☐
- 5 FLAMINGOS ☐
- 5 PIGEONS IN SCARFS ☐
- 3 HAMSTERS ☐
- 3 SEASON TICKETS ☐

## THE PENALTY

- 5 GOLDEN BALLS ☐
- 3 SEASON TICKETS ☐
- 3 FOAM FINGERS ☐
- 3 CLACKERS ☐

## BIG SCREEN

- 5 GOLDEN BALLS ☐
- 3 BUTTERFLIES ☐
- 3 CUPS OF COFFEE ☐
- 3 RADIOS ☐
- 3 PINK BALLOONS ☐

## HIGHBURY PARK

- 5 GOLDEN BALLS ☐
- 5 PIGEONS IN SCARFS ☐
- 3 ORANGE SODAS ☐
- 3 BAGS OF BALLS ☐

## CUP FINAL

- 5 GOLDEN BALLS ☐
- 3 TOILET ROLLS ☐
- 3 CLACKERS ☐
- 3 FOAM FINGERS ☐
- 3 SEASON TICKETS ☐

## VICTORY PARADE

- 5 GOLDEN BALLS ☐
- 3 FOAM FINGERS ☐
- 3 BUTTERFLIES ☐
- 3 CATS ☐

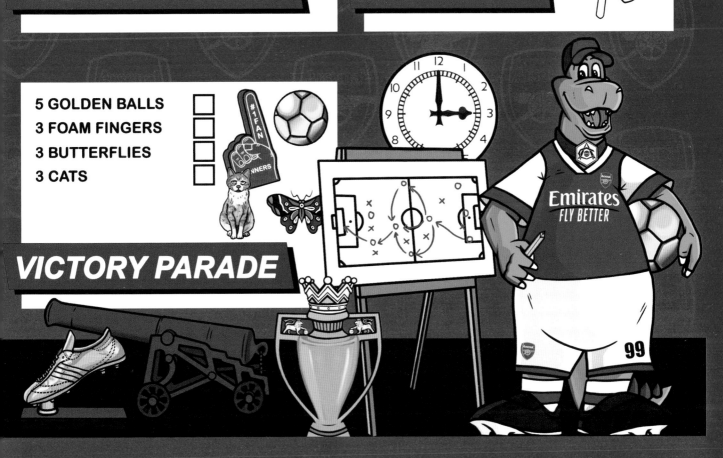

99

# SOLUTIONS

SEE YOU SOON